John Pe

—Ulster

Haunbook

John Pepper's
—Ulster—
Haunbook

Illustrations by
Rowel Friers

Foreword
by Billy Simpson

Appletree Press

First published and printed by
The Appletree Press Ltd
7 James Street South
Belfast BT2 8DL

Text © The Estate of Frederick J. Gamble,
1986
Illustrations © Rowel Friers, 1986

First published in Britain 1987

British Library Cataloguing in
Publication Data

Pepper, John, 1904-1986
    John Pepper's Ulster haunbook.
    1. English language—Dialects—
    Northern Ireland
    Rn: Frederick Gamble   I. Title
    427'.9416   PE2586

    ISBN 0 86281 183 X

9 8 7 6 5 4 3 2 1

Contents

Foreword

by Billy Simpson

At almost any time over the last 27 years, whenever someone enlivened a sentence with an expression that had wit, colour and the kiss of Ulster about it, somebody would invariably cry, 'That's one for John Pepper.'

In a world where language changes, adapts and renews itself with new manners of speech to suit the age or the fashion, a great deal of what makes our talk so colourful may be disappearing. If that decline has slowed a little in the last three decades it may have been because John Pepper taught us that our Ulsterisms were something to delight in and not be ashamed of. The cold electronic soul of the word processor cannot give birth to a description like 'He has a quare mooth for coolin' soup'. Or understand the impeccable logic of an Ulsterwoman who says, 'It was a lovely dress. It would have fitted me if I could have got it on.'

The Pepper column and the books provided a window to a rich heritage of colourful language that defies category and most of the rules. Their author, Fred J. Gamble, had a gift for capturing and recording our conscious and unconscious humour ('It'll not take me long puttin' in an hour'), our malapropisms ('The army threw an accordian around the area'), our spoken shorthand that can condense an entire sentence enquiring whether or not a companion has had his lunch into just one short, sharp sound, 'Jeet?', or for the verbose, 'Jeet yit?'

All of us have heard these and other Ulsterisms, but until Pepper set them down in print for us we hardly realised they were there. Or that they were special and part of our quality as individuals in a world where individuality is being ironed out into a kind of trans-Atlantic computer-speak. In his own way John Pepper rescued some of that individuality for us in a way that touched the heart as well as the funnybone.

For Ulster exiles around the world, his books have become a touch of home, to be read and reread to evoke old memories and perhaps warm a weary spirit on a dark day.

He did not live to complete his work on the *Ulster Haunbook,* his final book, and it is shorter than originally planned. But there is much to enjoy in it and again it is illustrated by the brilliant drawings of Rowel Friers. The John Pepper column was unique. The man who created and sustained it for nearly three decades was irreplaceable.

Joey's Bowler

'Nice one,' Joey said.

'I like it,' George answered. 'Thought it was just the job. Picked it up only last week.'

'Just the job alright.' There was a faint note of patriotism in the tone.

The two men, bowler-hatted, were on their way to the funeral of Harry Carter. There was promise of a good crowd. One that would have pleased Harry, who was a man for whom everybody had a good word. He was into everything, never missed a funeral. Besides the usual important organisations, Harry was a leading light in such bodies as The Safer Streets Association, Cut Down on Supermarkets, and The Control of Bad Building Organisation. A lot of them were societies which usually lasted a month or two before disintegrating.

'Cost you?' Joey asked quietly. He had an abiding interest in bowlers. The one he now displayed with pride was kept in a Bell's dozen-whisky box on top of the wardrobe in the back bedroom. The box had been borrowed from his off licence. Every week the hat was brought out and tenderly brushed, handled as if it were breakable.

Fifteen years ago Joey had bought the hat for £5. He considered this a small fortune at the time, but it was a good make. It was after he had seen a BBC interview with a leading Orangeman who was explaining the details of his

regalia and emphasising his pride in his bowler. It was emphasised that the hat had cost £30 and that the price in London ranged up to £100.

Joey was convinced there was money in his bowler. It would be a shrewd investment. Besides, there was now the fact that he had kept a careful record of its history. It had appeared at ten Twelfth parades, at least twenty-five processions, nineteen funerals and nearly nine weddings. Its size, too, was an advantage; 7½ wasn't far from average and was easily adjustable.

'Your missus was telling the wife the interest you take in that bowler is powerful,' George was saying. 'Wife was talking to her last week. Ye know women.'

Joey gave him a sideways look. At home his interest in the bowler was a sore point. The last time it had been an issue he had been accused by his wife of 'worshipping that oul hat'. It had been a rough encounter, for they did not often argue. 'If you'd spend your time on a couple of budgies it would make all the difference. *At least a body could see a budgie and hear it sing.*' In the argument the budgies came off second best.

He nodded without enthusiasm at another mourner heading for the funeral. Beside him was a man in a cap. 'Mac's could do with a bit of a brush up,' he said in a low voice.

'Everything Mac puts on could do with a good brush up,' George said. 'Did you ever think of selling that hat?'

'Selling it?' Joey echoed, trying to keep his voice calm. 'Outright?' This was out of the blue.

'That's right. Outright.'

'Might do, George. One day.' George wasn't exactly the buyer he had in mind.

'I don't suppose you'd have a price in your thoughts?' George prompted.

'It would all depend, George.'

'Look Joey. You know bowlers inside out. I know you wouldn't be asking the moon. I know it's a good article. I just thought it would make a nice wedding present for the daughter's husband-to-be. She's to be married in a couple of weeks.'

Joey nodded. 'I don't think so.' There was no future in this conversation. All those Twelfths; all those years of cleaning; and his hat, his treasure, finishing up as a £20 wedding present, hardly worth looking after, probably a wee lad's toy.

No, it was worth a lot more. 'Look, George,' he said. 'I'll look around for something and let you know. Thanks for your interest.' He fixed it more firmly on his head.

The next moment they were swallowed up in a group of mourners.

When a Woman Shops

Women rarely shop in silence. It is a fairly safe assumption that a comparison between the comments made by a swarm of Belfast shoppers and those of a group in Manchester, Cardiff, Glasgow or Middlesborough would not leave Belfast in the ha'penny place.

I'm dyin about this dress. Blue's my colour. The only thing is it fits me too soon.

She told me when she's down in the dumps she always gets herself a new hat and I said I often wondered where she got them.

My man's very thoughtful. He always washes his hands before he comes to bed. You couldn't say that of a lot of them.

14

'I was in this shap in Ballyclare yesterday and I was countin my change. The oul shapkeeper lucked at me, an he says, "Can ye no count or can ye count none?" They're a funny lot down there.'

'Woman dear but that's serious weather we're gettin, isn't it?'

'Rain! Nobody could say that was rain. Sure there's hardly enough to cover a lafe.'

'I saw that the woman in front of me in the supermarket would have a pay slip as long as a fat man's pair of braces so we moved till anor check point. You havta play with the head.'

'I didn't get over the door all day yesterday the way my corns was leppin.'

'I asked the girl for half a yard of red ribbon and said to mind she didn't cut the finger off herself. She give me a quare look.'

"It was terrible in Majorca. Everything I put on stuck to me. My feet were burnt aff me."

"No matter what style I get, as soon as I open my mouth you'd know where I came from."

"I nivver like to ring him up for he's awful hard to life."

They All Remember Andy

One of the consequences of getting long in the tooth is that things that once brought delight become sources of irritation. This doesn't just mean that you are no longer able to relish a lollipop or go tree-climbing.

Take the case of Andy, the Belfast Ormeau character of the twenties, lively memories of whom have flooded in to me from Ormeau Road veterans now living as far apart as Kent and Caledon, to say nothing of Birmingham and Clitheroe.

Andy's chief characteristics were a capacity for drink and a talent for irritating the law. He had a record of more than two hundred convictions for drunkenness.

Yet the former Ormeau Road citizens now scattered far and wide remember Andy with affection and associate him warmly with the happy days of their childhood. Mention of his name brings back those joyful boyhood years when legless Andy was the butt of their mockery, their parents' bidding ignored. Many of the latter spend hours jeering at Andy — but when their children were involved it was a different story.

Every area in the country must have the equivalent of Andy. As is the case with most down-and-outs, his background was a mystery. Some said he was driven to drink by a cruel father, others that his father had been too good to him.

Certainly his career as a 'character' was a lengthy one. To

run up such a toll of court convictions, besides the appearances when he would be allowed off with a fine, took a fair period of time.

It made an Ormeau youngster's day when Andy would stagger into their ken and the exchanges could begin.

Some days the youngsters would start the ball rolling by shouting, 'Come on, Andy. Chase the peelers.' Andy, it is reported, would roar back, 'Get away from me, ye wee ruffians. Get back to yer ma's apron.'

Letters recalling Andy and the happy memories cherished of him poured into me for weeks. One correspondent suggested that the man merited a statue.

There are suggestions that he was a boxer because of the shape of his nose, although it is more likely that this was the result of one of his contests with the police than a professional encounter in the ring.

The police must have been relieved to see the last of him, the arrival of the day when drink wasn't enough to send him thrashing and roaring through the streets looking for a fight. The one place where there was regret was among the staff of the prison canteen; apparently he was a first-class cook.

Usually it took six to ten policemen to control him when he was at his worst. Once four officers started to move him to the barracks in Donegall Pass, half a mile from the spot where he was causing trouble. After an hour they had covered only a few hundred yards.

Even the calling of a Black Maria was of no avail until someone had a brainwave. There was an undertaker's nearby which had a large sliding entrance door. Andy was pushed inside and the door pulled closed. The vehicle was then reversed to the door, which was quickly opened. 'Freedom,' thought Andy, and made a dash, only to find himself locked in the arms of the Black Maria.

Strange indeed that the luckless Andy should be recalled

by so many people (except maybe policemen) with such warmth, while those whose contribution to Ormeau was much more worthy are completely forgotten.

Agony Column of
The
Ballyragee Gazette

Ballyragee Gazette, Saturday, April 20

Sir, Can nathin be done about the milk packets? Me an my man spill the half of the milk before we can get one open. I hadda stap my husband from usin the hatchet on one yesterday. He was jumpin mad, an I wussent far behine him. Even the Black an Decker didden do the job. If nathin's goin till be done we're goin back till the battle next week.

Ballyragee Gazette, Saturday, May 28

Sir, We have a wee lad next door who's turnin intil a right wee nosey. I hope this letter will get something done about him. I don't know if his ma puts him up to it. He gets her steps and puts them up agin our fence. Then he sits and stares intil ar garden for all he's worth. He does nathin but stare. I keep wonderin what he expecks. I wonder is he hopin I'll cut his throat, because I might.

Ballyragee Gazette, Saturday, July 10

Sir, My son's mad about his flute ban. I doan mine that but he's started to bring them home at night to practise. They take over his bedroom, about eight of them, an start blowin, imaginin themselves to be eight Jimmy Galways. One of these days they'll crack the roof an the neighbours'll complain. How do you handle a neighbour who asts you to get the flutes stuffed? What do you stuff them with?

Ballyragee Gazette, Saturday, June 11

Sir, The orr day I was feelin terrible peckey an thought to myself after readin the death notices in the paper, 'Them that goes quick don't know they're livin.' See me? I'm thankful every day I doan fine anor fackulty gone. I was at the health centre an ast the nurse to make sure I gat an extra dose of tablets because last week the battle was half empey. All she give me was a glare when I toul her. You'd take your end at some people these days.

Ballyragee Gazette, Saturday, September 5

Sir, Please excuse paper. The wee lad's da made paper airplanes with what wus left of our note paper and all a cud get me hauns on wus the chile's exercise jatter. Cud ye tell me why it's so hard to get a stamp these days? It's nathin but a waste of a body's time tryin to get one at night. The man across the street from us collects them and he has hundreds, his wife says, but ast him for a 12p one an ye getta luck. Yu'd think he wud hev one he cud sell you to post a letter. What does the man collect them fer? Justa stick in an oul book?

Ballyragee Gazette, Saturday, November 15

Sir, I'm pleading with you to help me about my husband. He isn't a bad soul. He never bates me round the house. But he keeps goin till the big fights an it's terrible what this does till him. He comes home from them hoarse as a horse, sayin he has lost his voice because he was cheerin the fella that gat hammered. He always seems to cheer the one who gets knacked out. Even if he is hoarse he keeps sayin in his sleep, 'Hit him. Use yer elbow. Ye hev it in ye to make that mouse under his left eye into a bloody big rat. Have a go at the blirt.' He goes on for hours. Is there a ramedy for this?

Ballyragee Gazette, Saturday, December 20

Sir, I married a shoemaker. We have eight sons and a daughter. He mends all their shoes. I onny wonder shud I hev married a windey cleaner?

Such Good Neighbours

'We've always been awful good neighbours,' Mrs McQuish said. 'Close, I would even say. Well, till a while ago. I'd give her my recipes and she'd give me hers. A right wee woman. Couldn't do enough for you when you're in trouble. I've known her and her man for a good wheen of years now. She can make the most of herself. I'll say that.

'What gets me is that she likes to put on airs. She has a lovely fireplace in her front room but to my mind it's a bit fancy for a wee house like theirs. Sticks out like a sore thumb. You could see the Number 4 on their door if you had on a pair of dark glasses on a foggy night. That's the kine of woman she is.

'Don't think I'm being critical, mind you. Not one bit. I know she had a video before we did but that didn't bother me. She was welcome to it.

'Right enough her man couldn't do enough for her. Bought her a silver teapot for their anniversary and it was round the street in seconds. Mind you I had my doubts about that teapot. Maybe it was silver, maybe it wasn't. Looked to me like as if it fell aff a larry.

'Hear her talk sometimes an she gets on as if she'd been educated. Educated! Latta nansense. She was at the health clinic one day for an injection and told the doctor, "Give me a double dunt for I wasn't able to come last week."

'Hanest, she has an accent you could shake a stick at

when she's not thinkin. The pair of them get on as if they own the place. Lord and Lady Muck from Clabber Hill wouldn't be in it. It's the God's truth.

'Just because her man's eyebrows meet he always says it gives him an air. It's what she told me. Did you ever hear the like? The man's as common as dirt, so he is. He may be handy about the house — and when it comes to that he could see my man far enough — but puttin up a shelf isn't everything. There's more to life than a shelf.

'See her? She has a heart of corn if she would only let herself go. I'm not sure if it's her or her husband who's to blame. The way I see it I'd put all the blame on the same woman. Her Sammy would be alright if he was left alone.

'An there they are livin four houses from us and we haven't spoken for three years. Not since that night we looked in on them and we were havin a cup in our hauns. My man said as a joke, "An how many yards are you from the corner, Sammy? Sixteen? Eighteen? More?"

'"What are you talking about?" Sammy said.

'"Ach, man dear," my man said. "Saturday night there. You were at the bowling dinner, no doubt. Remember? It was about three in the morning. I asked you if I could give you a hand. 'Go to hell,' you told me, so I went on. You were busy anyway measurin the walls. Man you were doin the quare job."

'"He wasn't doing any such thing," says she, all indignant. "Sammy would never get into a state like that. Sammy wasn't measuring any walls."

'"You could have fooled me," says my husband. "For goodness' sake, Sammy, you were stoned out of your mind. No harm in that."

'"I'd rather nothing more was said about it," says yer woman.

'"Anyway I only intended it as a joke. No harm done," my man said.

'But here she is to us when we were goin: "It isn't a very nice thing to be insulted under your own roof."

'"Pity you spoke," I said till him afterwards. "Great pity."

'"It was nathin but a joke," says he. "I didn't intend any harm. The man was legless."

'Anyway it was only an excuse as far as she's concerned. I know rightly. It all goes back to the time my man wouldn't go guarantor for hers when he wanted to buy that Minor. He never forgive us. And nire does she. Anyway a woman whose bed's like Paddy's market at six o'clock at night can't be up to much. You can't get away from that.'

I nivver like to ring him up for he's awful hard to lift.

What Your Stars Are Saying

Most Ulster people put considerable faith in their stars. Few would be happy if they missed their horoscope. They will follow it even more faithfully if they are assessed in their own speech. 'I'm goin back till bed' indicates a poor day ahead. 'Mine's clinkin' shows that the stars are in your favour. 'It's like seein what yer tea cup tells ye — natta bitta harm in it' is the generally accepted view.

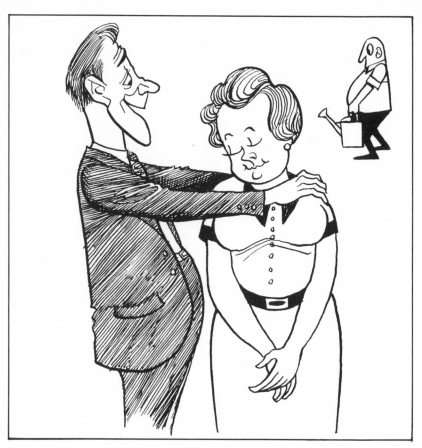

Aquarius
Jan 21 - Feb 19
CALL HER A WEE DOTE

This is a period when you should speak more affectionately
to your wife. It won't do a bitta harm when she's been to the
hairdresser's to say, 'Yew luck awful nice.' You'll find it will
pay divvies. Man dear, just think what the wee woman does
for ye, workin her fingers to the bone.

Pisces
Feb 20 - Mar 20
TIME FOR REDDIN UP

Git out the brush an map. It's tidying up time. Tho out all
the junk you can get yer hauns on (just watch your man
isn't among it). The things you'll nivver need again onny
clutter up the house.

Aries
Mar 21 - Apr 20
GIVE UP THE PAN

You will be meeting someone who will knock you aff yer feet. Watch out, for you've bumped into people like that before an it didden do ye a bit of good. Men should tell their wives, 'I'm sick, sore and tired of the pan' an the cheers will raise the roof.

Taurus
Apr 21 - May 21
HAIR OF THE DOG

You'd be a wise man to ease aff the hair of the dog. Don't always suspeck people who give you advice. Just because you're musical doesn't mean you should think you're above everybody and go roun like death warmed up.

Gemini
May 22 - June 21
EASE AFF ON LETTIN ON

It's a lat better to have your frens saying you're dead nice than call you a big-head. You're too fond of goin at things like a bull at a gate but when you don't you're alright. Blue may be your lucky colour but don't put *all* your money on Linfeel.

Cancer
June 22 - July 21

A SLAP IN THE EYE

Give your feet a right good steepin for you cud be futtin it the quare bit before long. This is no time of the year for hirplin. Expect a bit of a surprise at home. It could come from either himself or herself, and cud give ye a right dunt up the couter.

Leo

July 22 - Aug 22

A QUARE SHOCK

It's wrong to get the notion that a good supply of drink in
the house will always get you by. You aren't all that better
than the next fella. You'll win more frens if you don't let
people think you're a bumptious oul skite.

Virgo
Aug 23 - Sep 23
JUST IGNORE THEMMUNS

You'll do remarkable if you cure yerself of bein an onion. Everybody likes you because you don't keep thinkin of yerself every minnit of the day. Just you stay the way you are.

Libra
Sep 24 - Oct 23
DON'T ACT THE GULPIN

If travellin anywhere make sure of the time for you're not
much use in a hassle. Gettin intil a panic does nobody a bit
of good. Besides, there's no sense in gettin yerself known as
a big softy.

Scorpio
Oct 24 - Nov 21

BUY THE WIFE FLIRES

A good time to buy a car. The stars are in your favour if you don't let the dealer take you in. Also a good time to buy your wife flires, or take her out for a surprise supper.

Sagittarius
Nov 22 - Dec 20
STAP TH' GULDERIN

Far too often Sagittarians get their friends' backs up by bawlin their heads aff at them. There's no call to raise your voice. People will lissen if you speak softly. Just mine the Ruby Murray song.

Capricorn
Dec 21 - Jan 20

YOU COULD BE SKINT

Don't go up the walls if you win a bit on the pools. That's the kine of money that nivver lasts. In one ear and out the other. Mine the days when you were short of the readies an nobody wud len ye a bean.

My Stummick's Churnin

He was happy with his patient and the good relationship they had established. Mrs Gourley was in her sixties and had varicose veins. He was from the East and while his medical knowledge was growing in assurance there were times when his patients had him guessing. Understanding clearly what they had to say was an important element in healing, he felt.

He put away his stethoscope and closed his bag. 'I'll see you again next weekend. You're coming along like a blazing house.' The phrase was one he had discovered a few days before and he was surprised at her blank look. The words would need another look, he decided.

'Doctor, when you're going out the door,' said Mrs Gourley, pulling the blankets round her shoulders, 'Would you ask my daughter if she would bring me a jar?'

'Certainly.' He hurried out, his mind on his next patient, a gallstones victim who smoked thirty cirgarettes a day, all low-tar.

At the bottom of the stairs Mrs Gourley's daughter was waiting, and he told her, 'You're mother's doing fine. She would like you to take her up a Scotch.'

'A Scotch, doctor?'

'That's what she said. She told me to tell you she would like a jar.'

'Don't be daft, man. She's cold. All she wants is a hot

44

water bottle. If I took her a Scotch she'd have a fit.'

'Sorry,' he said hastily and hurried away. It was yet another item to add to his list of localisms that spelt danger.

This included one expression that had set him off on his voyage into the vernacular when a woman patient told him, 'I'm not at myself.' Another lady had summed up her complaints with, 'My stummick's churnin.'

He had had some difficulty in coping with the request, 'Doctor, for God's sake could you take me out of myself?' In such cases his usual ploy was to ask, 'Could I have a few more details?' This helped to make it clear on another occasion that the woman who told him, 'My man's bad' did not mean her husband was a pillar of wickedness.

One early pitfall he had encountered came in the statement, 'My guts is up the pole.' It was a condition which, fortunately, did not call for a heart transplant.

The lady who insisted that she'd 'hadda discharge' was another early find. He had had a feeling of triumph in assuming she'd been made redundant.

'I can keep nothing down' and 'Everything keeps coming back' were other treasures of his bedside glossary. Noted less for their ambiguity than for their style were the statement, 'It's my legs, doctor. They're giving me gippo. What's the right time?' and the request, 'Could you do something about my husband? He keeps talking like he has a bit in his mouth.'

Another unexpected moment came when a patient asked, 'Could you hold my teeth till you examine my chest? For God's sake don't drap them for we're going to communion on Sunday.'

She was classed with the woman whose request was for another bottle of the medicine he had prescribed. 'You remember it?' she said, 'It was the colour of a ginger snap dipped in tea.'

'I know it,' he said cheerfully, thinking to himself, 'It's like hacking your way through a wood.'

Small Ads

Few things give away a community's life style or its general range of interests like the small advertisements placed in the local shop. They can betray the advertiser's religious beliefs, state of health, age group, social class, politics, hobbies, profession, even his financial standing. In each case that follows the spelling has been corrected.

The examples given are not intended to attract answers from interested parties; telephone numbers are therefore not included.

```
3 DOZ. UNCRACKED MILK BOTTLES

TOP CONDITION.
£30 the lot O.N.O.

EXCEPTIONAL OPPORTUNITY
```

<u>GOING FOR A SONG:</u>
SET of HOLIDAY POSTCARDS, mainly
from Spain. (Two from Corsica,
three from Isle of MAN) Stamps
removed

Twin Buggy, double cover
Changeable from Union Jack to
Tricolour.Can also be altered
to ALL BLACK, showing neutral.

Needs slight repair.

<u>£25</u> O.N.O.

Andersonstown district

Ballymena postman has
25 pairs non-matching socks
on offer. All Christmas presents

NO REASONABLE OFFER

REFUSED!!

FORTY POTS OF MARMALADE

gone slightly off. Happened
only last week. Could be of
value for compost heap.
NO REASONABLE OFFER REFUSED.
Ballygomartin Road area

FOR SALE

Collection of Rock Records. Only 4 un-
cracked. Bargain at

£1 o.n.o.

Cromac St. district

for sale:

set of golf clubs, all but 3 in prime
condition. Were smashed by owner after
throwing away Cup Final match when 4 up.

Bag has Co. Down badge

for sale

3 one-legged pairs trousers.
Excellent material. Tailor made.

Queen's Rag Night relic

CHEAP for quick sale

LOST!

Siamese cat answering to name of

BALLYBEFOREYE

Lost in Greenisland area. Well-
behaved but doesn't like horses
or fish. All white

REWARD OFFERED!

FOR SALE

Quantity of broken slates. Could be of use

to D.I.Y. enthusiast. Delivery taken care of.

QUID the lot O.N.O.

(Sandy Row district)

FOR SALE

      12 horse-shoes for decorative
purposes. In prime condition. At £10
a real giveaway. Reason for sale -
owner bankrupt.

           (Snugville St. area)

For sale:

   Walking Stick. bears initials
G.H.T.V.E. Has covered 1,000 miles
but has big mileage left
Family heirloom.

     Malone Road area

BOWLER HAT

As new. Looked after. size 7¼.

Used for fourteen Twelfths, six

funerals and three weddings.

     £15 O.N.O

(Antrim Road locality)

Wake Etiquette

Anyone invited to a wake for the first time should remember that it differs considerably from any other gathering of mourners. It should be taken for granted that the corpse, whether covered or not, is often addressed as if he was present in person.

For example, when invited to 'drink the health' of the deceased the convention is to gesture towards the coffin and say with heartiness, 'Your very good health!'

Similarly, there is nothing unusual about it if one of the guests says to the corpse, 'Your wife was tellin me that the day before you passed away she bought you a pair of long johns an the next day it was so bitter cold she was sure you would have felt the good of them and put them on you. She did right, now, didn't she?' The mourners will think nothing of waiting fractionally as if expecting confirmation from the deceased.

Nothing transforms a person's character like a wake. The greatest villain unhung will be made to resemble a paragon of virtue.

'He was a giant of a man in this townland' is sure to win murmurs of approval, besides a quick response to the speaker's signal that his glass is empty.

A wake newcomer would be well advised to go into training. It is no place for a man who cannot hold his drink. The drinking, the revelry, the crack, the stories have been known to last well beyond six a.m.

Confusion can sometimes arise, for anything can happen. During the revelry at John McDade's wake it was discovered that so many people had been sitting on the edge of the bed on which he was laid out that it had collapsed. The chief mourners rose to the occasion by deciding to prop the corpse on three chairs until the undertaker arrived. One of them called to guests below, 'Three chairs for John McDade.' Instantly came the response, 'All together, boys. Three cheers for John. Hip, hip . . . .'

As the night progresses the women tend to drift away. Inevitably in the early hours 'men's talk' takes over. The question will even be asked when the audience is all male, 'What on earth did he ever see in that string of misery of his? Dammit, his death rattle had hardly died away before she had a notice stuck on the door, "House Private". But then, of course, he wasn't a man to ever expect the worst. Only last week there he got a bad hair cut and when he told me about it he said, "Ach it isn't as terrible as a short leg. Sure it'll grow again." '

A sense of humour can be extended beyond the grave, as happened at one big Tyrone wake. The story was told of the deceased that shortly after buying a brace of prize cockerels he had had to see the doctor about a pain in his leg. 'I don't suppose it could be crowing pains, doctor?' he had asked with a grin. The mourners heartily agreed that 'He could crack a joke with the best of them.'

At another farewell one woman, taking a cautious sip of her drink, said, 'My man went up to see him an kem back with the word that he'd be under boord before night. The next night I was in bed when my man came in to tell me the poor soul had got a seizure. I might as well have got up, it was such a shock.'

It can be said of a wake that at least it provides an opportunity to commune with the dead. This happened on one occasion when the deceased was told through his coffin,

'I'll never forget the night we had last Christmas there. God but you were goin well, an herself nivver heard a word about it. There you were stannin on the bar-room counter singing Danny Boy. It nearly brought the roof down. Ye could have been on TV. D'ye mind the night? Ye must mind it.'

There was general agreement that the night must indeed have been a memorable one.

Belfast for Aliens

Attendants in the leisure centres are invariably caring and attentive. Occasionally they'll look at you as if wondering 'What on earth are you doing here?'

Banks treat the public with complete disdain at lunch time. They are then rigidly closed. You must keep your cash in your pocket. It's no go if you want to cash a cheque.

Barmen usually disgruntled. Give the impression of being grossly under-tipped.

Not terribly talkative. Safest subject to mention is Barry McGuigan.

Black taxis are plentiful but the other passengers are usually resentful of the stranger. The driver's only contribution to any conversation is 'Where till?'

Bookshops are of a good standard but there should be more of them. Those in existence are too far apart.

City buses should not be expected to provide the last word in comfort. A large number have un-upholstered seats. Drivers keep their distance.

Good cup of coffee not easily to be had. Standards vary tremendously. Best bet is to try a café with harrassed looking waitress with dirty finger-nails.

Hamburgers sold in Wimpey's superior to those elsewhere. Much better value and service on a higher scale.

Ice cream standard appallingly low. Take-away packs not worth buying, as a rule.

Nurses are nearly always in good spirits. They enjoy being chatted up in a light-hearted way. Often are victims of over-zealous discipline.

Pedestrian zones are used too extensively by motorists. Walkers are treated by drivers as if they shouldn't be alive.

Place to go for the Marks and Spencer store with the biggest cash turnover of any in Britain. Southern accents of the shoppers may give the idea you're not in Belfast. These are the Dublin bargain hunters who come up in droves because prices are lower in the North.

Police officers are generally friendly and helpful. They'll chat affably but always underneath will show caution which they aren't going to throw to the wind.

Public toilet attendants constantly wear a disgruntled look. They give the impression that they have just discovered a pools coupon they forgot to post which would have won them £50,000.

Street wear not a patch on English cities. Women's fashion shops don't reflect what is worn outside. Prices high. Men dress with indifference.

Supermarkets are uncomfortable for shopping. Not enough space for shoppers. Rush hour parking arrangements are maddening.

Traffic wardens are as sharp and efficient as they come. They carry an air of having heard your excuse many times before and they're getting weary of it.

Unkempt gardens are in the minority compared with those tended with loving care. Some suburban houses are a paradise of colour.

Ulster-English Glossary

Language is forever changing. Some words are everlasting. Others pass. The glossary in my *Ulster-English Dictionary* lacks words about which people keep asking me. There are old words in use like *fouf,* new ones like *gatturted.* This glossary may be of some light-hearted help in keeping the balance.

Ackaweigh, often used instead of 'Catch yourself on' or 'What d'ye take me for?' Shows you are well aware someone is trying to put one over on you.

Ajar, everyday word for a drink, usually a Scotch.

Allayezjuke, warning call used by a bus driver when the vehicle runs into a disturbed area, with bullets and missiles flying. The idea is for passengers to take refuge under their seats.

Amaidimanaffer, indicates that a prospective buyer of a car showed interest by offering an amount below the asked price. Does not necessarily show eagerness to buy.

Amgoan, when a party guest gets to his feet and uses this word it should not be taken he wants to spend a penny. The implication is that he is anxious to leave, to go home.

Bard, something lent to the speaker: 'I bard it from a fren.' 'He's a right lad is Mike. I bard a quid from him a week ago and he hasn't tortured me to get it back.'

Bars, country expression for gossip. Someone returning from a visit to friends will be asked, 'What's on the bars tonight?', the aim being to find out what the latest gossip is. In common use in Co. Tyrone.

Barls, part of the anatomy, the intestines: 'Dacter, I'm havin bother with my barls. They haven't shifted for a week.'

Blow-in, a recent arrival in the district. Anyone who hasn't been a resident for at least three or four years. 'She's only a blow-in' will describe someone living in the area for such a period.

Bracklin, word used in country areas for broccoli: 'The bracklin's good this year.'

Broad, often used to describe someone's religious faith, particularly that of a Protestant: 'I know he's a broad by the way he walks.' 'He's a broad alright for I heard him whustlin the Sash.'

Canty, neat: 'She's a right canty wee bit of a thing.' 'She has a canty wee body.'

Chase, blasphemous utterance. Can be used by someone who has missed a bus or train, as in, 'Chase I've missed her.' There is also, 'Chase the rain's on again', or the critical, 'Chase, see what you've gone an done?'

Chay, expression used on farms to pacify excited cattle.

Clatchin, a sitting of eggs. No specific number is meant.

Collies, trade name for cauliflowers. Confuses those unaware of this, who often take it to be a breed of sheep dog.

Conah, end of the street, often a popular assembly point: 'Seeya at th' conah.' 'That fellah's nathin but a conah boy.'

Cronyn, expression surviving in country areas for the purring of a cat: 'D'ye hear pussy cronyn away there?'

Cummindown, showing intention of paying a visit: 'I'll be cummindown bout sax, all bein well.'

Dawnder, a short walk, taking your time: 'I just went down the street for a wee bit of a dawnder.'

Deddon, exactly what is wanted. Indicates to a shopkeeper that your change is completely accurate. If you buy something at 25p, give him 50p and he gives you 25p, you will say, 'Deddon.'

Desprate, a condition beyond hope. Someone who is in the last stages of despair, or cannot be relied on: 'Jimmy's a desprate man.'

Ditchwater, country expression which means water in which the dishes have been washed.

Eejit, someone lacking in intelligence: 'He's an absolute eejit, hasn't a bit of sense in his head.' There are also stupit eejits: 'The stupit eejit set the house on fire.'

Evansnaw, strongly affirmed denial: 'Evansnaw, I would never do a thing like that.' 'Evensnaw, it wasn't me.'

Fares, matters of state: 'We want to be able to luck after our own fares.' 'We're weel able to handle our own fares.'

Fashion, usually an accompaniment with chips when eating out, as in 'Fashion chips'.

Fate dealer, sometimes used to describe car agents: 'He's a Fate dealer. Ye cud depend on him.'

Fern, not related to this country: 'He's the fern minister. He has nathin to do with us.' 'He does nathin but hannel fern fares.'

Fillum gore, person keen on film going: 'If ever there was a

fillum gore it's big Mary. She's seen *Gone With The Wind* eleven times.'

Flar, ground meal of wheat or grain: 'I sent the wee girl for a bag of self-risin flar.'

Forgivin you, generally implies a threat, as in 'I'm forgivin you a clout on the gub if you don't behave yourself.'

Fouf, said of a snapping dog: 'That accordeon is making the wee dog fouf. Wud ye stap playin.'

Fractions, differing sections of the populace: 'When the fractions get at each other's throats anything can happen.'

Gatturted, said of someone who has received an injury: 'Wee Georgie was hit by a car last week and gatturted.'

Gooms, something about which you usually have to see the dentist: 'My gooms is all swelled.' 'My gooms is awful sore. It must be something I ate.'

Gravelling, covering applied to pathway: 'I did a bittaff gravelling, so I did.' 'I wasn't grovelling, I was gravelling.'

Harpus, indicative of thirty minutes past the hour: 'See ya at harpus ate.'

Hartell, indicates that word has reached the speaker: 'Haretell yer lavin your job.' 'Haretell she an her man are separatin.'

Hartscalded, implies that the speaker's heart is broken because of misfortunes: 'My heart's scalded, so it is. He never gives me a minute's peace.' 'He has my heart scalded with the way he drinks.'

Herant, a reference to a person's aunt: 'Herant's away with the ban again.' 'See herant? ye cudden be up to her.'

Hussent, shows inaction: 'He hussent done a han's turn this six months.' 'Him! He hussent put his fut over the doorstep for long enough.'

Jeet, form of lunch-time inquiry: 'Jeet yet?'

Lafe, growth from a tree: 'There's hardly been anough rain to wet a lafe.'

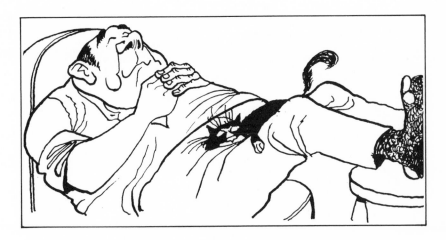

Lift, hear easily: 'The daughter's child's a great wee infant. I can lift every word she comes out with.' 'My man's bror's an awful man to lift. Ye couldn't make out a word he says.'

Maffit, denotes that a habit has been stopped: 'Thanks all the same. I know the stout's good but I'm affit.' 'Pint? Thanks a million but amaffit ni for a fortnight.'

Mankeepers, name for newts. Children living near canals are warned to keep their mouths shut 'In case a mankeeper jumps down yer throat.'

Mended, restored to health: 'You're luckin quare and well mended.' 'Yer rightly mended after yer holiday.'

Moganny, otherwise mahogany, tropical American tree used for furniture making. In many Ulster homes they have their New Year celebrations at moganny: 'We're having a New Year party in our house for magonny.'

Near yourself, to have a narrow escape from injury: 'That bus missed you by the skin of your teeth. You were awful near yourself, so you were.'

Or tern, indicates that it isn't your round when buying drinks: 'It isn't up to you to buy. It's or tern. Put your haun back in your packet.'

Parish, not necessarily one's church or ecclesiastical area: 'The oul lad wudden do without his parrish every morning.' 'He's dying about a boul of thick parrish.'

Peerinaids, spectacles: 'Joe's like a bline man if he isn't wearin his peerinaids. He went to a match once without his glasses an he was up the walls. Wanted his money back.'

Penson, refers to a person on whose opinion much can rest: 'It penson her.' 'What we'll do penson the missus.'

Ploutin, walking through wet grass, or along a flooded road: 'I've been ploutin through this stour for the last half hour. I'm soakin.' 'You'll have a quare bit of a plout to get home after all this downpour.'

Pubbilick, the general populace, the people: 'I always say it's a matter of pubbilick opinion. This is a damacracy, after all.' 'The pubbilick hasta hev the last work.' 'The more pubbilick houses there are the better, I always say.'

Quap, Belfast's Co-Op store. A bus driver will call, 'Yiz said yiz wanted aff here. This is the Quap.'

Richey coo, used for calling home the cattle.

Rightly on, indication of the time of day, that the hour is getting late: 'You wanta know the time? A cudden say for sure but it's rightly on.' Can also indicate a person's state of sobriety: 'I saw him after the pubs shut and mind you he was rightly on. He musta hadda skinful.'

Salary, popular vegetable: 'We gat some lovely salary the day. It was quaren cheap. Salary's alright, my man says.'

Sallis, contentment, usually found in a garden: 'I always fine a latta sallis in ar garden. It's great to set there fer the sallis it gives you. You can't bate it. The flires give you a latta sallis.'

Scundered, annoyed, offended: 'I was all scundered after what she said.'

Seempoler, cricketer with a special bowling technique.

'Big Sammy loves watchin the cricket. Says he'd love to be a seempoler. Give him a ball, he says, an he'd make the wickets fly. He's the quare man for watchin when there's a tess on.'

Semley, recently suspended Northern Ireland Assembly: 'That Semley up at Stormount, sure they did nathin but talk.'

Sempying, has the same meaning as bucketing, implies heavy downpour of rain: 'I was foundered comin home. It was sempying the whole way. I gat soaked to the skin.'

Sir, indicates a woman to whom the speaker wants to refer: 'Sir. The one over there with the red beg.' 'Sir alright. I'd know her face anywhere.'

Skelpin, smacking delivered to a wayward youngster: 'I givver the quare oul skelpin for cummin home late.' 'She didn't get in till all hours so I give her a skelpin.'

Skinnymalink, unduly thin person: 'Her and her da are nathin but a coupla skinnymalinks. It runs in the fambly.' 'Jinnie was a skinnymalink from the day she was born.'

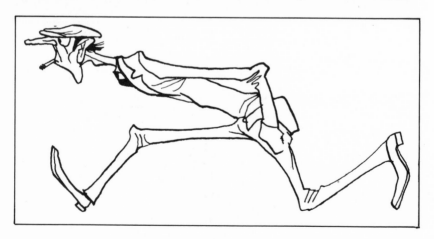

Soredust, usually plentiful in carpenter's shop: 'I'm goin down to the carpenter fir a lock of soredust. We use a lat of it because of the budgie.'

Souple, an active person, full of energy: 'Lizzie's awful souple. Nivver affer feet.' 'She was always a terrible souple wee girl.'

Stravague, purposeless walk, as in stroll: 'Away and take a stravague up the back road and see if that'll keep ye quiet.'

Thile, church passageway between rows of pews: 'He made a laughing-stock of the weddin. He went down thile with his shoes nat laced. He made a mackery of it.'

Timidation, threatening behaviour: 'This is a terrible place for timidation.' 'If you aren't careful you're liable to be timidated. Even if nobody bathers you you can still be timidated.'

Unaided iron, what many people are fighting for — a United Ireland: 'Fella in the pub said he wud like nathin more than a unaided iron. I told him to get lost an he didn't like it.'

Wile tame, pet that has been exceptionally well tamed: 'That wee dog of ours is wile tame.' Also used in the same context as 'That's a wile wet night.'